So Much To Unlearn

MAUI THE WRITER

First paperback edition November 2020

Book design by Amirah Morris

Maui The Writer

So Much To Unlearn

Unlearn

Discard (something learned, especially a bad habit or false or outdated information) from one's memory

Hopeful Romantic

I have fallen in love with the idea of a person before I have completely known who they are, a hopeful romantic to say the least. Even after being heartbroken some of us refuse to give up on love. Some of us refuse to believe that our fairy tale ending isn't out there right now waiting for us, to come along and change our whole perspectives on romance. Some of us are so eager to experience true love that we prematurely give the titles, benefits and the most intimate parts of ourselves to people who put forth no effort into even being blessed by us in that way. For some reason or another we ignore every red flag that is telling us, "Stop praising people for bare-minimum treatment." You know exactly what bare-minimum treatment is, it is when we allow people to come into our life and feed us crumbs of consistency, never enough to become full, just enough not to starve but not even close to ever being fully happy and satisfied. But we stay with them, hoping to pull more out of them, hoping that they will ease the hunger we are craving.

We crave something deeper than a few slow-response text messages, FaceTime calls and sex that leaves you wondering why you even still talk to them. Nothing makes you feel special outside of the intimacy that you share, so you ask questions like, "When are we going on a date?" "Damn, so you're going to go the whole day without texting me?" We try to force things out of people that they do not naturally want to do for us. Where are the boundaries and the non-negotiable things we should have when we come into dating?

Yet still we allow ourselves to fall head over heels in love with the challenge that is attached to the person we are always thinking about, praying that our love will change them. So in the moments when we should not be giving them shit, we give them more. We hope that the love we give to them will transcend into them becoming even better than we hoped for.

How many times will it take to be put in situations where you are pouring everything that you have into someone just to end up feeling like you are constantly getting the short end of the stick or like they have left you with nothing? We have to constantly remind ourselves that we are setting the tone for all the relationships that we encounter and decide to involve ourselves in. Nobody should be able to come into your life treating you less than how you treat yourself. If you have created your own happiness the company of someone else should be able to add to what you have created not come along and take what you have created, leaving you with nothing at all. We can be hopeful; we just can no longer go through this life being naive.

It is our job to believe people the first time they show us that they do not care about us. It would be foolish to convince ourselves of something other than what we have seen with our own eyes.

Alfredo

He hasn't even mentioned taking you out on a date, shows no signs of courting you properly or wanting a relationship, but somehow he is at your dinner table eating your world famous Alfredo. Our desire for companionship, or our attachments, can never be stronger than the boundaries and the expectations we have for the people who come into our lives. We know exactly what we want. So how is it that we continuously find ourselves accepting some bare-minimum-ass shit? We overextend ourselves to people who put no effort into showing us they value who we are and we convince ourselves that we can love them into loving us or seeing how much we have to offer. Our offers will be enjoyed by people who do not know how to do anything more than just receive. Then, before we know

it, the signs that we saw in the beginning
are the reasons we are leaving and
feeling as if we poured everything we
had into someone and it wasn't enough.
Learn when to be honest with yourself
and say, "This is not what I want." Until
you know what it is you want, you will
continue to settle for whatever it is you
are offered.

Romanticize

To think about or describe something as being better or more attractive or interesting than it really is; to show, describe or think about something in a romantic way.

One

Tracy

I could imagine how I would love him before I ever knew he was interested in me. I am not sure how strange that is, but I would daydream about what I would get him for his birthday if we spent it together and I even had bridesmaids for our wedding in mind. It has been 11 days, 23 phone calls, seven FaceTimes and one date since I met my soulmate. If it counts for anything, my new man, Kyle, is a handsome, well-dressed Libra who owns his own business. I'm an Aries that by no means is ever shy about what she wants, but I can't stand the thought of rejection. On a lighter note, say happy birthday to your girl Tracy, I just turned the big 30 this past April. I am excited to even be dating again after the mess I went through with my ex. I thought I would never even so much as like a guy again.

Anyway, tonight is date number two and Kyle should be here any minute now. I have my hair slicked into a nice bun, the baby hairs are laid but I didn't want to do too much, I have on a black maxi dress paired with all black So Kate Louboutins. We're only going to dinner, but I am so happy to see him. It feels so good to be excited about someone's company and to finally be getting out of the house. Don't you love how good it feels when you first meet someone? The butterflies in your stomach or the random songs that have you cheesing so hard. The beginning feels even better when you have voids you're trying to fill with companionship, but I guess that's a conversation for another time.

"Ding." Text Message Kyle
"I am outside."
I give myself just one more spray of my Chanel perfume before I leave.

Kyle is double parked in front of my house in his all black Audi R8 with 5% tint on the windows. I get inside and greet him with a kiss on the cheek; unsure of where we are going to eat I am just enjoying the ride. He has such good taste in music. He knows that I am from Philly and have only been living in Chicago for a few months because of work. Not to jump to conclusions but I am guessing he keeps playing a lot of Meek Mill songs because he knows I love Meek of course. I am in the passenger seat enjoying myself while making snapchat videos of myself as I lip-sync, "Going bad."

"So what do you want to eat?" he asks me.

"It doesn't matter to me, but I love seafood."

"Oh ard, cool"

I remember telling him Eddie V's is my favorite seafood restaurant, I wonder if he remembered. We don't talk much during the ride, but I keep trying to create small conversation.

"So how was your day?"

"It was cool, didn't do too much."

"Oh, okay… Well, mine was really good. I actually got a promotion at work today, so I'm super excited."

"Niceee, that's dope."

"Yup."

We get to the parking lot for dinner and I notice that we're pulling up to Applebees. This is not even close to what I meant when I said I like seafood. When I look at him as we get out of the car he has the nerve to say, "What? I like the drinks here."

I think to myself, *You know what? It's not even about where we go, it is all about enjoying each other's company. Besides, Eddie V's really is overrated anyway.*

"Tracy, you drinking tonight or you just gone eat?"

"Ehh, I'll have one drink, I have to be at work by six for training."

"Oh ard."

I ask him about his business and where he sees it going in the next couple of years. We talk so much that I feel like I have known him forever, but I still have never asked him what is it that he is looking for in a relationship or even if that's even what he's looking for. I think a part of me likes him so much that I don't want to ask him in case I don't like the answer, which turns into me not liking him. I also feel like I should ask because what if I start investing even more time into someone who doesn't want the same things as me right now? Either way I look at it, there is no win in holding back, so I'm just going to ask.

"So Kyle... What are you looking for in a relationship?"

"Like what do you mean? I'm just chilling right now."

"I mean what are you looking for in a girlfriend or are you even looking to be serious with someone?"

"Honestly, I'm just trying to find someone to vibe with, I'm not really looking to be putting titles all on a situation and having to feel obligated to do certain things."

"Certain things like what?"

"You know, the whole having to take someone's feelings into consideration all the time."

"You'll change your mind; you just haven't met the right person yet to make you have a change of heart."

He gives me this flirty look and responds, "Change my mind then."

I just start blushing super hard; he's so handsome and I feel like I'm just melting whenever he looks me in my eyes.

That wasn't necessarily the answer that I was looking for, but what's wrong with just enjoying someone's company without pressure? I know I want to be in a

committed relationship and I really like
Kyle; plus I already cut off all the other
guys I have been texting because I only
ever want to talk to him. We talk so much I
don't even see how he would even have
time to entertain anyone else but me.

On our way from dinner I text my best
friend Brittney to see if she's up. She's so
hype to know how the date went.

Britt: Okay girllllllll what happened?

Tracey: Nothing, it wasn't even really
a date; it was Applebees and a few drinks.

Britt: Applebeeeessss in my Soulja
Boy voice. Girl, how you let him take you to
a place that has crayons and a coloring
menu for kids?

Tracey: It's about spending time
together; it doesn't matter where we go...

Britt: Yeah, you can think that shit. I
want to be wined and dined.

Tracey: I want to have sex with him
tonight, you think I should???

Britt: Let me send you money for a 2 for 20 if that's all it takes for you to give it up.

Tracey: Byeee lmao I knew I shouldn't have asked your ass shit.

Britt: Text me when you get home and keep your vagina to yourself.

As we're driving to my house he stops at the gas station to get gas. As he gets out he leaves his phone in the car and it's unlocked on the music playlist screen. It is taking everything in me right now not to go through this man's phone. I am a grown woman, I am not going through someone's phone like we're in high school, he's not even my man at that. I saw this post online the other day that said, "If you have to go through their phone you shouldn't even be with them." That was a good quote, but for now there's no harm in a quick peek. I'm going to just look at the text messages really fast and see if I see any girl names. Before I even get a chance to scroll through really fast the first thing I notice is heart eyes and a "I miss you" text that he sent to an Amy 17 mins ago.

We were on that cheap-ass date 17 minutes ago and you texting a girl you miss them? I immediately put the phone down and get nervous when I see he's finished pumping the gas. He gets in the car and I am trying to act super normal, as if I was not just in here being an FBI agent. Can you believe, he gets into the car and asks, "You cool?"

I give off a very dry, "Yeah, I'm fine". I don't say anything the whole ride. I don't even have anything that I want to say besides, "Who is Amy?" There is nothing more annoying than wanting to bring something up but you can't because of how you found out. So all I can do is just sit here and be mad in my head. But the truth is I'm not fine, I voluntarily made myself exclusive to a man that said out of his own mouth he isn't looking for a relationship and I am sitting here mad because he is still texting females. As we're pulling up to my house for him to drop me off he asks, "Can I come in and use the bathroom real quick?" I just let off a very dry response of, "Yeah, sure."

I really wanted to say no, but I don't think I am at the level of petty to tell him that, his ass should have used the bathroom when we were at Applebees like I really wanted to say.

We walk inside and I direct him to where the bathroom is. As he walks past the living room to get down the hall, he compliments on how nice my house is. I go into my room to sit on the edge of the bed and take off my heels, thinking to myself, *Why do girls put themselves through this type of pain to look nice? My feet are killing me! Walking around for hours in shoes that hurt, just for you to look nice for a person who may not even notice it or tell you that you look beautiful.* Good thing I like to look nice for myself because I would definitely have been upset waiting for a compliment tonight.

Kyle comes out of the bathroom that is right across from my bedroom and says, "Ard I'm done, I'll text you when I get home."

Even though in my mind I am upset about the text message I saw, for whatever reason I respond, "Why are you leaving already?"

He pauses for a second then he walks closer to me at the edge of the bed, taking my Louboutins out of my hand, standing over me looking so good and just says, "I don't ever have to leave if you don't want me to."

My common sense is screaming inside of me that I shouldn't do what I am about to do, but the woman in me who is always overextending herself to emotionally unavailable men thinks doing more will change someone.
I want to change his mind about being in relationships and not wanting to settle down. I am a goddam good woman, and he will see that. I know that sometimes men

aren't used to having a woman who would do anything to see that they are happy or satisfied so they don't know how to handle it. Kyle is just like a lot of men who do not know what they want because they have never had it.

So I make up my mind and I pull him on top of me and I let him have his way with every part of my body. He is caressing me so softly, even as he's kissing and touching me everything is intense. I am living in euphoria right now. I'm not sure if it feels good because I am so attracted to him or if it's because my ass don't have no business having sex with him. This is everything I imagined it being. He's choking me while we're having sex and licking on my neck. I already liked him but, damn, I think I like him even more now. My love language is physical touch and, even if this is wrong, right now I am being satisfied in a way that I haven't been in so long.

After we're done I go to the bathroom to get him a rag and take a shower. He's already sleep by the time I get back into bed and I must say it feels so good not to be in bed alone tonight. I lay my head on his chest, put my leg over him and even though he appeared to be sleep he leans over and kisses my forehead. Those forehead kisses get a woman every time. I fall asleep and I feel peaceful lying right up under his arm.

I wake up early the next morning to get ready for my training at work and I wake up Kyle too. He's so cute when he's sleep so I didn't really want to wake him and if I didn't have training I would have been fine with us lying in bed all day being lazy. I asked him if he wanted me to make him a quick breakfast, but he declined. He said he was fine and would stop and get something on his way home, but I know a good date, some good sex and with me offering to make him breakfast, he's going to want to be in a relationship. How could he not want to be with me? I am smart; I'm beautiful; I have a great sense of humor, not to mention I'm very successful.

I found myself at work all day thinking about him. He hasn't texted me all day and I don't want to start thinking that he's already acting differently because we had sex. I will be the first to admit that's the problem with having sex too fast, we start worrying about shit that didn't even bother us before. Then all of a sudden since I had sex with you I am offended by the fact I haven't even received at least a good morning text.

Hours pass by and it is finally time for me to clock out from work. On my way home, I stop by the market to get something to make for dinner. Taking my time in the market, I am grabbing things I do not even need. I am almost done getting groceries when I get a text message from Kyle with the eye emojis asking me, "What's up?"

I was thinking about not responding right away, but a part of me wants to because I'm happy he finally texted me, so I reply, "Nothing, just getting some food for dinner tonight."

We make small talk through texts for a while and then he asks, "What you making me for dinner tonight?"

I smile, assuming that he wants to see me again tonight and that's why he asked me that, so I respond, "What do you want for dinner?"

He says, "How about Alfredo?" Little does he know, I make the best Alfredo, so Alfredo it is.

I end the conversation with, "See you at 9 then."

I get home and begin cooking and blasting love songs. I know Kyle said that he isn't looking for a relationship, but I still feel like he hasn't experienced the type of vibe that I can give to him. Dinner is almost done, the house is clean and smelling good. I call Kyle to see how far he is, but he doesn't answer. So in an effort for me to kill time, I decide that I am going to take a shower and shave before he gets there. I am in the shower for at least 15 minutes, I dry off, lotion my body and put on my pajamas and he still hasn't called me back. I send a text message with the eyes emoji and no response.

Two hours go by and at this point there is no way he's sleep and I am getting tired trying to stay up and wait for him. I call him one more time and it rings twice and goes to voicemail. I feel foolish as hell right now to have to even be going out of my way to keep calling and texting someone that I made dinner for. He should be calling and texting me if I am the catch. If I am so much of a great woman like I say I am, why am I overextending myself to a man that has already expressed that he had no desire for a relationship and now has me up all night waiting for him? I decide that I am going to take my ass to bed. I put all of the food away and get in bed.

Soon as I am getting ready to turn off my TV, Kyle texts me at what is now 1:42am, "You up?" I am so annoyed at this point. I am annoyed with the fact he even has the audacity to text me this late, after having me waiting all this time and I am annoyed with the fact that I replied "Yes". As much as I wanted to take my good advice, as much as my ass knows better, the curiosity of where this might go is killing me.

When you know better you do better. We set the tone for how we expect people to treat us, so I guess anything else that happens after all of these damn red flags that I have saw is all on me. Until then, I am going to go warm up his Alfredo.

Hennessy

You can fall in love
Just don't end up hurt
Because you have grown impatient
Or falling in love where there is no love
So you end up putting in more work

You feel like you are getting older
And not exactly where you thought you
would be
So your eyes start playing tricks on you
Seeing potential in everyone that you meet

He has not invited you out to dinner
So you invite him over to eat
With a bland conversation that lacks
substance
So you have another drink

One more double shot of Hennessy will be
enough
And you can also use the excuse of being
Drunk as to why you let him fuck

But you've just been craving to feel
Something
That reminds you that you are alive

And not just existing
Feeling like you should have just stayed
with the last guy
But he had a girlfriend, that he said didn't
really mean shit

But you still fell in love, because he was on
some trick shit
And would buy you anything to help you
Cope with
The reality that you will never be his main
chick

I wish you a love, that's all yours
And a dick you do not have to share
You've spent all this time working on you
And the fact that you still haven't found
someone who sets your soul on fire
Got you feeling like this love shit isn't fair

It was easier to settle
Before you found yourself and you didn't
care
Now the only way to come to you is correct
And they have to meet you way up there
I wish you a love
That doesn't feel lonely laying right next to
Them

The fastest way to steal your own joy is to keep looking back on your past so much that you forget to live in the moment.

Preparation Station

Can you be prepared for something you do not truly believe you are completely worthy of? You do not have to answer the question now; taking your time to actually think and sit with that question is perfectly fine. The reason for me asking you that is it is so easy to say, "I've been asking God to help me find my soul mate," or "I need the Ciara prayer." I am just unsure as to how can we possibly wholeheartedly believe that we deserve and are ready for something that we have never experienced. Think about it; some of us have encountered love several times in our lives and the shit never lasts. Although we may still be hopeful that eventually we will end up with who is meant for us, we unconsciously move more cautiously the next time around to avoid getting hurt or ending up in the same situation again with a broken heart.

How do we enter something healthy and not question it after all we have experienced are things that did not work out before ? By working on ourselves? Healing ourselves first? Or maybe one of my favorite quotes, "Find yourself then find me." It is all so much more easier said than done, but it really is the truth. It is your job to work on yourself so that you can enter new relationships with an open mindset and heart. You will steal your own happiness and will not be able to enjoy the experience of taking things one day at a time if you are constantly obsessing over whether or not this is the right person or if it's going to work out. People always eventually reveal who they truly are and whatever happens was meant to turn out that way, so why drive ourselves crazy in the process?

We can't assume a person will lie and cheat on us just because the last person did. Now we are in new relationships showing them more of our insecurities than our love, not trusting people who have never given us a reason not to trust them. You deserve to be happy. You deserve to experience the love that you give to everyone else and to have someone treat you kindly. I would hate for you to go through life having had been through so many fucked-up relationships at any capacity that when someone comes along and shows you different you do not think that things like this can happen to you. You think that there must be a reason they are being nice, they only are nice because they want to have sex with you or they must have a girlfriend they are hiding. Whatever the case may be, allow yourself to get to know them and see for yourself. I would like to believe that you're a good person and a part of why good things are beginning to happen to and for you is because you have been patient and have been putting into the world everything that you wanted to receive in return.

Running

A part of me wonders what are you
running from
Have you been so hurt deep
You think it's best
That you just run from love

Or have you grown exhausted
Giving so much of yourself in places
That made you feel it's just not enough
I can't run behind you
But if you ever get tired
Just call me and we'll do some catching
Up

I love that you're ambitious
But to take your mind off being lonely
And filling voids
You drown yourself all in your business

Who will you celebrate with
So wrapped up in this journey of self
love
We forget

That once you find yourself
It's okay to find someone to share
yourself with

If I had to choose
I would gladly give every part of myself
To you
But you'd probably run
Out of fear that history will repeat itself
And you'll be in the middle of
The same shit the last person put you
Through
I just can't take the blame
For someone who didn't know what to
do with you

So if you're going to run
Let it be into the arms of someone
Who gives a little more than they take
Who won't take the things you do for
Granted then throw your love
Right back in your face

Whew I'm scared

To those of us who do not know when is the right time to date, because we have learned how to enjoy being single and cannot seem to like another person longer than a week, this is for us. I always felt like it would be hard to know if you are ready to date if you are not dating. Of course we can just simply feel like we aren't ready, but what about when we feel like we are ready but we just are not sure? With that being said, when you are at a place in your life where the love that you have for yourself is running over in abundance and you feel you have enough to share with someone else, do not be afraid to try. The love for yourself is not here to replace the love of another person. We will never be able to satisfy our own needs in a romantic way. You were put here to love another person and to be loved in return, at whatever capacity makes you the most comfortable. I think what is most important is that when we decide to date we do not forget or neglect all of the inner work we just did for ourselves. This means entering the dating world doing things differently than you have in the past, throwing away all habits and concepts that haven't worked in the past and most importantly not neglecting the love that you have learned to give to yourself just because someone is around now who cares for you. Even in a relationship or dating, your self-care days are still important, you finding time to be alone is still important and you continuing to remain your own individual while creating memories with another person is still possible. We will start dating again after being single for a while and be so excited that we have found someone we like that we throw away our individualism and go straight to merging our lives with that person. Now it's two months into dating and you have neglected your self-care Sundays and are with this person 24/7 and do everything with them. You go to the movies together, the supermarket, the mall, the gym, the club, the bank and sometimes the nail salon. Then, by month four, everything about them annoys you because you are around them so much. It is your responsibility to remember that you can still love and be your own person. You do not have to be afraid because what will be different this time than the other times is that you know who you are and what you are looking for. There won't be a need to paint the red flags we see in people any other color, we won't have to settle out of loneliness because we have learned how to be alone and we won't have to force ourselves to like someone when we know how to make ourselves happy now. Either the chemistry is there or it just isn't. If you feel like it is taking forever for you to find someone you even like a little bit, I hope your ass doesn't get discouraged by that. Remember it is quality over quantity. It was easier to find a partner when you did not know yourself that well and you were easily impressed by anything presented to you. The more we grow, the more we set the tone and the standards for how we want to be loved or deserve to be treated, the harder it becomes to just settle. So do not force yourself to see the beauty in something that just simply is not what you want.

Wishful Thinking

This is all hypothetical
And wishful thinking
Unless you're willing to do the inner
work

But broken can't fix broken
So we can pause on the love stories
To work on ourselves first

If I can't make myself happy
It would be selfish of me
To expect you to know how to
To depend on you for my light

You still haven't addressed your
Childhood traumas
So you're always triggered
So here comes the arguments and
Pointless fights

My pussy can't be your only sanctuary
Of peace
Because your not in tune with your
Emotions

So you always feel like the problem is
me
Taking up all your time
Won't heal my insecurities or attachment
issues

You leave
Then I miss you
Don't go, just stay
You're not in the mood but we have sex
anyway

This is the one thing that we can agree
on
So the cycle just goes on
Ain't no problems being solved
Just putting flowers on top of bullshit
And dressing up our mess

Sex ain't gone heal no wounds
Only hide them
They still need air to breath
But you so afraid to be alone with
Yourself
You'll rather spend your life creating a
Future you don't really see

But eventually you'll have to be alone
with yourself
And be forced to find happiness inside
Of you
Happiness is a state of mind
But it will always be wishful thinking
Unless you are willing to do the inner
Work

Companionship

A feeling of fellowship or friendship
-Company

Two

Jasmine

Every day I find myself counting the minutes at work until it is time for me to go home. I have the same routine every day, me rushing to get into a home that feels so empty. I have so many great things going on for myself and what I crave the most is companionship. My best friend said, "I'm single because I am a Virgo and I just overthink everything." Maybe that does have a hint of truth in it, but I just feel like I forgot how to allow myself to fall in love. One part of me wants to be in love and there's this other part of me that isn't even sure if I am emotionally equipped for the shit that love comes with. I guess when I really think about it, I am my own worst enemy. How do you crave something so much but never allow it close enough for you to receive it? I will meet a guy and, after a week, he has turned me off and I am back to being comfortable with just counting the minutes until I am off of work and back in my bed. I find things that I do not like about someone so fast. One slight inconvenience then I am already thinking about how this can't possibly be my soulmate and a relationship with them will never work. Am I looking for some type of perfection that doesn't even exist? I know that if I am patient then exactly what I want will find me. I just hope that I am at a place in my life where I am able to be receptive; a place where I truly believe that I am worthy of the things that I pray for and won't run out of fear when they arrive. I have just been so afraid of wasting my time with someone or falling for the wrong type of person and ending up hurt that I forgot how to just live in and enjoy the moment. The type of pain that comes with loving someone who turns into someone you completely do not know is a feeling I do not want to experience again. To be honest my ass doesn't need any more of things that don't kill me but make me stronger. I have learned enough lessons from love to last me a lifetime; all I want now is to find someone to create memories with. Maybe that's what this is all about and what I should try to do, be selective about who is in my company but not be too afraid to enjoy the journey. Everyone I meet isn't my potential soulmate or someone I will fly off into a sunset with. Some people that we meet are just meant for us to learn something from or to be our friends. As much as I want to be happy, I want to also know that I did not just decide to settle one day, after feeling like I would never find what I was looking for or, even worse, go back to someone who had hurt me in the past because at least I knew what to expect or I convinced myself that there was nothing else out there for me. I am affirming that I am deserving of love, I will constantly do the inner work to become a better person and I know that the love that I have for myself isn't meant to replace companionship. Loving myself is enough until what is meant for me finds its way to me, at the right time. But until then, I won't beat myself up emotionally feeling like my life isn't complete; everything is aligned exactly the way it is meant to happen.

Alone doesn't always mean lonely, just like a relationship doesn't always mean happy.

MAUI THE WRITER

The Choice Is Yours

You are in control of choosing the kind of love that you desire. The only reason I say, "Choose" and not attract is because I know a good person will attract many people, the hard part is deciding what you are going to choose. Are you choosing what you deserve or are you impatient and allowing your loneliness to choose based on what's available to you at the moment? Nobody should be able to come into your life and give you significantly less than the love that you give to yourself. Why would you even be interested in receiving less than? If you find yourself somewhere accepting some bare-minimum shit ask yourself, *Is this all that I feel like I am deserving of? Am I afraid of being alone? What are my expectations when it comes to how I want to be loved? Lastly, can I reciprocate what I require from others?* When you date with no intent and have no expectations, you allow people to come into your life and give you whatever it is that they want. If later on down the line you decide to have expectations and you start requiring more, it will only seem like you have changed. They will say things like, "You asking for too much" or "You do not appreciate anything I do." This is only to make you change your mind or try to convince you that you should be grateful for whatever it is that they give you. This is why it is so important to express your expectations in the beginning; only a person you should not be entertaining in the first place will run away from the pressure or what you require. A person who knows that they can meet your requirements will not run, but they also want to know that they will be loved the way they love. Not loved in the exact same way but with the same passion. That's why you have to make sure you are willing to give the things you are expecting to receive. A person who understands value is going to understand your worth. Real will recognize real and you won't have to force the pressure on them, they will fold if they aren't the one.

A Mom First

Going on my self-love journey was difficult the first time when I got out of a relationship with my child's father. As parents we want to give our kids everything that we had and did not have growing up; in my eyes that meant giving my son a family, even if it was at the expense of my own happiness. Even if I was not happy or in love, it was my job to figure out how to be for the sake of my son; this is where it began, the idea that putting myself last would pay off for the greater good. We do this so much, at our jobs, with our families, as a student or staying in any place that we know takes more of our happiness than it brings. We think if we put everyone else's needs, wants and happiness before our own we will find some sense of satisfaction or happiness knowing we didn't do what was best but what made sense. I became so depressed in my relationship and at my job, feeling as if I did not know who I was anymore or what made me happy. I forgot who I was because I wasn't a priority in my life. Coming home to lie next to a person who didn't see me, who didn't value me, someone who had hurt me beyond what I could forgive but I stayed because I was afraid to start over. I had also hurt them too, so I'm sure they weren't happy either. Just two people who were broken and craved companionship more than the responsibility of working on themselves. So after years of trying I finally reached a place where I was ready for it to end. It wasn't after catching him cheating, lying or disrespecting me; it was during a time when things were actually okay. I had realized I spent so long begging for him to change and now that this better version of him was here, I was a completely different person. What he offered was no longer what could satisfy me. People do not realize the growth that you go through while waiting for them to change. What I required was so different compared to what I wanted five years ago.

So I left to go on this journey to find what makes me happy, what makes me feel whole or alive. I felt guilty at first because I did not know a life where I was put first, I only knew how to put people before me and appreciate my short end of the stick. During that journey there were nights when I would cry because I missed the comfort of the people who hurt me but would wipe my tears. I was afraid to be alone just as much as I was afraid of falling in love again. Even though everything I was doing was new to me, my first baby step was learning to enjoy my own company and be alone. I hated myself because I did not know who I was, I did not know what made me happy and anytime I was alone I would just cry, feeling like I broke up my family just for me to still feel so empty. I realize now that it was selfish to expect anyone to know what made me happy when I did not even know the answer myself. So I began having dates alone, trips to the mall or a good movie night by myself. I had to learn how to be my own friend first so that I would not be easily impressed by the first person offering attention.

I always hear people say, "I want to love myself more, where do I start?" The truth is you have to start with yourself, it's that simple. Be accountable and realize if you want shit to be different, you have to take a leap of faith and start doing things differently with no regrets

Hopeful

Feeling or inspiring optimism about a future event

Three

Dana

It is 7:45 a.m. and I cannot find my car keys or my son Mason's book bag. At this point I would probably lose my head if it wasn't connected to my shoulders. I finally find both after tearing apart my whole living room; now I am rushing to strap Mason in the back seat of my car and drop him off for another day of third grade so I can head to work. I drop Mason off and pull up to my job 12 minutes late, but on the bright side I am here. I am a nurse here in downtown Philly, so after work, errands and taking care of my son I am exhausted. My life might be a little bit easier if his damn dad did more, but that's another conversation.

As busy as I am with so much I have going on, I met this guy whose name is Jason. We have been dating consistently for two months but we only get to see each other on Fridays and Saturdays, those are the days Mason leaves for the weekend. I love that Jason understands that I am a mom, so he never even tries to see me during the week or complain about the two days he gets to see me. We have FaceTime dates during the week when Mason is sleep sometimes, where we both watch the same movies while we are on the phone. I wish I could explain how he makes me feel, from being a gentleman to being educated, family oriented, religious and handsome. In my heart I can see myself being with him. Even watching Jason's eyes light up as he talks about his own 11-year-old son makes me admire him even more. I have just never introduced my son to anyone, ever! Mason's dad has been in about four relationships so I pride myself on being the responsible parent who puts my child and his safety and needs at the forefront of all my decisions. I have been on dates but I never had a serious relationship since his dad because

I never really had the time most relationships require to build something. But lately I have been thinking; I just do not want to be one of those moms who put falling in love on the back burner and then their kids go away to college and they do not know what to do with themselves.

I know I have only been dating but how soon is too soon to introduce your kids to the person you are dating? If I wait a year then I will be disappointed if my son doesn't like him and I wasted so much time with him. If I do it too soon I will be disappointed if the relationship doesn't last. I think the best thing to do in any relationship is to take things one day at a time, not overthink it and let things happen naturally. If this relationship is going to continue to grow then them meeting is going to eventually happen, but this weekend would be perfect because Jason is going to have his son for two weeks. I do not want him to feel pressured or like I am moving fast so I text him and ask him,

"What plans do you and your son have this weekend?"

He replies, "I was actually hoping that we could do something with you and Mason."

I just sit there at my desk at work smiling at the text message. I am so happy that he was thinking what I was thinking. There is something that I still need to ask before I even agree to this play date I guess you would call it. So I text him back. "I think that's a great idea, but since I have never introduced my son to anyone, I just have to ask you this… Do you see a future between us honestly? I hate to even ask but I don't want to introduce my son to someone and then he doesn't see them again." He doesn't even respond but I can see that he read the text on his iPhone. I feel like I might have come off too strong asking him about a future. But he calls me an hour later greeting me in his calm deep voice.

"Hey Dana."

"Hey Jason."

He says to me, "I really like you and enjoy your company a lot, I would never introduce my son to a woman I didn't see myself being with, I suggested us hanging out because I do see a future with you."

I am silent for a few seconds only because I can't believe how straightforward he always is with me, everything is so much easier when a person lets you know exactly what it is. I just tell him, "Well, okay then, we can go to the movies, no house visits yet, only outings, I don't want any pressure on them and we will see how this goes."

He wraps ups our conversation with, "Okay sweetheart, sounds good, call me when you get off of work".

This doesn't even feel real to me right now. So many of us single moms get comfortable with being just that, "a single mom". Not that there is anything wrong with it, but we all want to be loved. Sure, we love our children, but that's not the romantic love that we all want as people. To even entertain the idea of someone wanting to build with me genuinely and meet my son wasn't something that I thought would happen anytime soon. Most of the guys I would meet only have thoughts like, "When can I come over?" or "Do you got a babysitter?" I never wanted someone to fall in love with the single woman part of me but not the mom that I am. Being one of those moms who sends her kid to the babysitter all the time so that she can go out all the time or on dates. Now you're dating a person whose main concern isn't you being with your child, it's them making sure you spend time with them. Putting what you love first will attract people with those same values. I know what I feel now wouldn't be happening with someone who wasn't family oriented or at least a parent themselves. I hope no mom feels the way I once did, as if they will never find someone who understands that their kids come first or that they can't always go out or you have to plan a baecation months in advance to make sure they can go. I hope they do not feel guilty about falling in love again. A person who cares about you will love the extensions of you, which are anything around you that you love also. I am allowed to be a mom, to be in love, to need self care days, to make myself happy and none of that takes away from me as a parent.

Prepare You

If you really want it
Ask God to prepare you
To make you whole
To help you grow
I know we fear the unknown
And would rather take things slow

But when you know you know
And when it's real you'll know too
It won't require force
Or you becoming someone you never knew

It will flow
It won't always be easy
But there's effort
And if we're in this thing together
Even when we're at odds
We know that it'll always get better

Ask God to prepare you for love
I want to drown in your love because it's extra

On top of what I've been giving to me
I'm able to love you effortlessly
While never taking away from me
Patience
What is worth it doesn't come easy

Don't be discouraged if you've been
Waiting
Be open
Let it find you
If you're running from it out of fear of
Being hurt
Then it will take its emotions and hide
Too

Love has two sides
Like a Gemini
Duality
The desire to fall in love but the fear of
you hurting me

Your happiness has no room
For your past
To haunt you and ruin things
Before they start
Or even begin

Ask God to prepare you for what you've been asking for
Because what's meant for you always works out in the end

If being with you interrupts the love that I have for myself I would rather just be alone.

MAUI THE WRITER

No Begging

How do we end up at a place in our lives where we become so similar to beggars? Begging for effort, begging for consistency, for a date night and shit; sometimes we beg for a good morning text instead of just the "GM" we get sent. Begging people to do things that they do not naturally or willingly want to do because if they did we would not have to keep asking. People who love you listen. I think the worst part is that you would easily go out of your way to give this person all of the things that they would not even give you a portion of. We so desperately want people to show us sides of them that they do not see any point in allowing us to see, but it isn't like we are going to walk away, we love so much and make so many excuses for them. Is this all for the sake of love or our inability to walk away from people who are just not meant for us? It is our job to have a clear view of our expectations, how we allow ourselves to be treated and what we choose to accept. Handing out parts of yourself to everyone and not saving any of "YOU" for "YOU" is how we end up begging. We would be more comfortable walking away from things we find difficult to leave if we were sure that was what was meant for us eventually does find us, so there isn't ever a need to settle.

Missing You

The hardest part of missing you
Is wondering if you missed me too
Or if something else has kept you
Occupied enough to forget
What I assumed I shared with you

Promises we made during a dinner for
two
I know better than to believe the
promises a man makes while inside of
you

I don't want to send that text
Make the call
Or reach out
If not once have I not crossed your mind

Because if it's better to have loved and
lost
I still valued the time
The pleasure was mine
These memories are fine

I just hope I don't deprive myself of
being happy somewhere else
Waiting for you to come along
So I can feel what we shared
Just one more time

I can tell how much you love yourself by the person you lay next to. I can tell your boundaries by the things you tolerate and your desire for peace by the things you forgive people for. Everything around you that you allow speaks for you, before you speak.

MAUI THE WRITER

No Looking Back

One of the hardest things for some of us to do is accept our role in the lives of someone we once loved. Accepting that certain things will never be the same and that the love might never be how strong it once was. It is okay to walk away from the person you are attached to. It is okay to still miss and think about them, but have no desire to keep putting ourselves through the same shit again. We disrespect ourselves every time we reach out to someone who doesn't care about us, every time we keep going back for sex knowing they don't value us and every time we try to be there for someone who doesn't appreciate us. No matter how hard it might be, the love for yourself has to come before the love you have for anyone else. If not you will be on a never ending cycle of continuously going back to someone who hurts you, because you are too afraid to let go. Don't let your attachment be the reason you are holding yourself back.

Two Pats On The Back

I was in a relationship for years on and off where two people were playing ping pong with hurting each other. Just going back and forth, taking turns with getting each other back. Even when I reached a place where I no longer wanted to make someone hurt the way they hurt me, which took time, growth and realizing they would never be able to understand how I felt, they continued to do whatever they wanted to do to satisfy their needs or give them temporary satisfaction. I wasn't going anywhere, so I thought, no matter how much he hurt me because I invested too many years to just start over with someone else. I knew what to expect here, but that new love, it hurts so much more with the first time they hurt you unexpectedly. So even though I wasn't happy it was familiar and safe in my eyes.

Everyone asks me, "When did you know it was time to leave?" For one it was time to leave once that person knew that I loved them more than I loved me; with knowing that, they knew they could get away with a lot of shit and I would find a way to forgive them. It's time to leave when the hurt they put you through overpowers the love you feel; when you cry more often than you receive flowers or texts saying, "Hey baby, I was just thinking of you, have a good day." When you are lying next to a person hurting because of the argument you two just had and they don't even want to roll over to talk about it because they run from tough conversations and being accountable. It was time for me to leave after years of me begging someone to change and they finally decided to change when they saw something else was making me happy, when I no longer was that hurt girl waiting for someone to see my value. I grew so much in the process of waiting for them that they no longer were what I wanted. I couldn't deprive myself of being happy by holding on to a dead situation. I wasn't even impressed by them trying to show me that they could be the person they were years ago. I have seen this show so many times. A person appearing to have changed and once they get you back they fall right back into their natural habits because they were never changing for themselves in the first place, they were only changing for you to take them back.

Fed Up

Annoyed or upset at a situation or treatment

Four

Nikki

"I know you see me calling your damn phone, stop fucking playing with me, Dave!" I know he sees me texting and calling his ass, he could at least say he's going to call me back. I just really can't stand him. I cannot stand how much the love I have for him has allowed me to hurt myself over and over by staying with him. It's like every other month I say I am leaving him; then he pretends that he is sorry and I end up right back with him.

He has broken me down so much as a woman. From the lying to the other women and the constant disrespect. The part that hurts the most is that I know I deserve so much better, but look at me, lying here wondering where he is at and what he is doing. My heart hurts so much over his raggedy ass because he knows I love him so much and he uses that to his advantage. He benefits from knowing that I will do anything for him or always try to make this work. I do not know anything else but him and I have never cared about someone this much.

I saw this quote today on this girl Maui page on Instagram and it said, "I can tell how much you love yourself by who you are lying next to." I felt personally attacked because I know that I am choosing to lie next to someone who doesn't value or love me. Maybe once upon a time there was love, but there isn't any love here now, just me holding on to old memories hoping he will change for me. I gotta turn this goddam music off, I am in here listening to Destiny's Child's "Is she the reason?" and this music isn't doing anything but make me cry even more. I am trying my hardest not to call his phone again or look on this girl page that I know he be creeping with to see if she posted anything.

I just want to know what are you doing that's so important you can't answer the phone or text me? He is on his phone the whole time when he's with me, so what chick are you with that you like so much you able to not even touch your phone when you with her? Shit, I also want to know why I am trying so hard to piece together a puzzle with someone who clearly is choosing something else over me as usual.

I am so tired of doing this to myself over and over. I could have been happy with someone else a long time ago or, shit, I could have been happier by myself. I have never in my life allowed myself to get in such an emotionally low place. I do not even feel good about myself anymore. I allowed this man to not only fuck with the love I have for myself but destroy my self-esteem too. I am constantly comparing myself to other women or feeling like there are things about myself that I should change. The old me was so confident. I would get dressed all the time, go out with my girlfriends and I used to travel so much. Now I am always laid up with him and even if I do go out with my girlfriends, if we're being honest, I can't even have fun because I am so worried about what he's doing when I am not around. I want my happiness back. I wish it was easy for me to walk away, but for whatever reason I just keep holding on.

Not after today though; tonight is the night that I am just going to start on my journey of working on myself. All the energy I have put into making this relationship work, I could have been pouring that same type of effort into myself and building myself back up. Starting today I am going to learn how to just love myself and give myself all the things that I have been begging for someone else to do for me. I know it is not going to be easy but it can't be any harder than what I have allowed myself to go through trying to get someone to love me how I love them. I am blocking his damn number too. I don't even want any closure and I damn sure don't need no last conversation for me to hear him say something that will make me forgive him and go back like I always do.

On the nights where I am lonely and I feel like I might text him, I am going to take my ass to sleep or go work out. No more being loved halfway, no more going back to things that always leave me disappointed; from now on it's all about loving me and everything else I will just pray on it.

Learn how to be done with things without, expecting one last conversation, a long paragraph explaining yourself, closure or farewell sex. Sometimes we've given so much that the only thing left for us to do is just be done.

The Truth

Tell me is it really true
Can your pride not handle the thought of
Losing someone who means so much to
you
Or do you fuck with me so heavy
Cuz I take you back after all the shit you
do

Slamming cabinets in this got damn
house
Saying I'm leaving your ass but I never
do
Because four years ago in May during
Our first date
That was the night I fell in love with you

Ignoring your flaws and patiently waiting
for the old you to show up
Saying I'm done with all the games I've
Grown up

Sitting your ass on the couch to face our
Problems head on and not run
Having conversations that you know
Would break my heart

But it would hurt me even more
If I had to hear it from her or someone
else

What is love
When you have emptied out your heart
and given it everything that you have
And it simply just isn't enough

When I love you more than I love me
But when shit hits the fan
I am wiping away my own tears
Patting myself on the back
Nobody shows up but me

Nobody is coming
But if you call me and need something
You know I'm running
Tell me what is love

One More Chance Baby

The hardest thing about giving a second chance to someone is not only wondering if this is the right decision but is it really a second chance? Are you giving them a second chance or accepting them for who they are and their continuous disappointing behavior? Is this a second chance or an excuse to go back like you always do because being without them it's just too damn hard for you to do right now? Second chances require someone to actually show you that they have changed and want to be different and that can't happen in three days and with a few "I miss you" texts. We do not even allow people enough time away from us to show us anything different, we kind of just forgive them to put our minds at

ease. We get tired of sleeping alone,
thinking of them and wondering what
they might be doing.
So we give them a second chance to be
with us again, but is it a second chance
to show us that they changed? We don't
even give people enough time to learn
how to treat us in the ways we feel we
deserve. There is a difference between
having company and having good
company.

Love isn't enough

If sometimes love isn't enough
And I love you too much to give up
How can I even trust myself
Looking into the eyes of the person who
has caused
Some of the deepest pain that I've felt

Kisses that used to heal me
To I love you's only when you guilty
Only when you see your life
Flashing before your eyes
And reality hits that you might lose me

Why do I have to threaten to leave your
ass just for you to choose me
This all should be different
You were never supposed to change from
who I met in the beginning

Or was I too afraid to lose you
That I created a fairytale
Out of what was only meant to be a
friendship
I lost pieces of myself trying to get you to
love me better

Trying to trust you after being disappointed
constantly

Craving attention because you no longer
make time for me
I'd do anything for your ass
But to you I'm never a priority
And its because you know the truth

That no matter what you do
My heart will always choose you

Until a man is clear on his intentions with you, you are single. Enjoy your life instead of waiting for someone to decide that they are sure about you. You are no one's second choice.

Easy Access

It always seems as if everyone is interested in you when you are no longer worried about them or when you are in a relationship. The only thing that has changed is your accessibility. People do not value what they can have whenever they want. You answer every midnight phone call, every two hour text message; you check up on them and are always offering them something. Some people see no reason to value what they did not have to earn or work for. We give people so much access to us and get mad that they do not appreciate our time or reciprocate what we give. Your accessibility is a part of the reason people feel like they can save you for later. We put aside things that we know are not going anywhere. We make reservations and go out to dinner when we are in the mood for something different, but we warm up those leftovers when we do not feel like cooking or going out. Now, don't get me wrong; I personally love leftovers, but the point is leftovers are not my first choice. Everyone wants to be where they have to make reservations. It is the exclusivity and the opportunity that they do not get often. But we value the food that we take home from those restaurants.

Start being more selective with who you are giving access to. There is no reason why people who give you nothing more than the bare minimum are able to call you for anything at any moment and you jump at their convenience. Stop allowing people to save you for when it is convenient for them. Be where someone will continuously view you as their favorite five-star restaurant they are excited about every day.

You bring too much to the table to allow someone to treat you as if they are settling for you.

Date Them All Sis

I was the girl who would meet someone, like them, daydream about our future and ignore every other person in my phone because the only person I wanted to talk to was them. Even if they had never mentioned anything about a relationship I would commit to them. I would become faithful to a person I was not even completely sure felt the same way that I did. All for me to do the most, find out they are still talking to other people and had no intentions of ever taking me seriously. Now my ideas of dating are getting to know people fully and talking to whoever the hell I want to. Until a man is clear on his intentions with me, I am texting back whomever I feel like talking to. I no longer prematurely commit, I take my time instead. Dating means going on dates, spending time getting to know each other. Preferably all of this can occur without sex or them somehow finding a way to come over your house and eating your world-famous Alfredo. This is the time when you find out who you actually have chemistry and a real connection with. Think about how many great people you have ignored by creating a relationship in your head that did not even work out or grow into anything more than a few dates and some sex; being faithful to the possibility of someone that you did not fully know. So if you are not sure, date them all and if none of them are what you are looking for then it is okay to date yourself in the meantime. Once we know what we want we aren't easily impressed by something that isn't close to it and we won't feel the need to attach ourselves to something just because that is what is available to us at the moment.

Wasting Your Damn Time

To the thrill seekers that love a challenge and fall in love with emotionally unavailable people, my heart goes out to you. Trying to get someone to tap into emotions that they aren't even in tune with inside of themselves. Some of these people do not even know who they are outside of the relationships that they attach themselves to and people who cater to the parts of them that they refuse to heal. It is not your damn job to raise anyone or cater to their bullshit excuses of, "This is just who I am." Running from accountability; conversations about relationships or anything that requires them to be vulnerable. What future is there in investing your time in someone who won't even allow themselves to be emotionally available to you? What can they do for you outside of physical satisfaction and pleasing you only sexually? Deep inside you know that you crave more than someone who can only stimulate your body while they abandon your spirit. It seems like the more we invest in these types of relationships the stronger our desire to have sex with them becomes. We settle for a sexual connection with them because that is the only form of intimacy that they give us access to. We crave only what they can give us since all of our other love languages are neglected by being with them. But in those few moments of the only intimacy that they know how to give, we feel everything that we wish we could receive from them on a daily basis. It is not your job to force or try to heal people who simply just need to go do the inner work. Even if you have the heart of a healer it is not your responsibility to be the therapist of people who refuse to look themselves in the mirror and be accountable.

Dating

To go out with (someone in whom one is romantically or sexually interested).

Five

Ashley

My problem is that I do not know how to date. Once I like someone, that's it. That becomes the only person I want to talk to and spend all of my time with. I cannot stand that I am so much of a hopeless romantic or always assuming someone will like me just as much as I like them. Putting all of my eggs into one basket, just for me to end up disappointed. This would not be so bad if I was falling for someone who had mutual feelings for me, but I always find the most emotionally unavailable ones who have the most healing to do. Is it too much to ask for just to find a person who loves the way that I love? For the sake of my heart, I have to learn how to take things slower and stop prematurely committing to relationships that I am not even in. I have probably turned down my damn soulmate while trying to prove to someone else that we could be perfect for each other.

I look back now and cannot even believe how much of myself I poured into men who never even slightly felt the same for me. It makes no sense to be the one putting in all of the effort to get to know someone while they show barely any interest in you. I guess the side of me that loves challenges felt like I could make someone interested in me. But I have broken my heart every time I have tried to do this; there is nothing you can do to convince a person, who has their mind made up about how they feel. They can only change their perspective on their own and by that time half of us wouldn't even want it. I wish I knew then what I know now. From now on I am going to get to know whoever I am interested in who is showing the same interest back for me. If they are serious about me, they will apply pressure to show me and I will gravitate to

where the effort is being shown. There is
no damn reason why I am putting all of my
energy into someone who hasn't even tried
to take me out on a date but can text me,
"wyd" all day. So from now on I am dating
all of them.

Effort is a reflection of interest, you won't have to beg for consistency from someone who is truly interested in you.

Gravity

I have been known to fall in places
That have no landing
No gravity
No longer in control of what is happening

I feel hopeless
Right next to a person
Who puts in just enough effort to make me
feel hopeful
Make me feel special

So we create these fairytales in our minds
of falling
Praying that they will be the one to catch
us
Which doesn't really take much
Especially coming from
A place where there was no love

Praising people for the bare-minimum
That would watch you free fall
If you love me hold my hand
Close your eyes

While the only thing thats on your mind is
I don't care where we land

As long as it is you that I am next to
Not focused on whose gone catch who
But out of all the people to fall with
A hundred times over again I would choose
you
If I am the one than prove it
It is so easy to say you will do anything for
a person
That does not require you to do shit

If I am the only person on your mind
Then don't lose it
Don't lose your train of thought

Then after a fight you are ready to give up
Or you forgot why we fell in love

Don't tell me to jump if you are not ready
Got me believing you would be the one to
catch me
Do not say you love me if you don't mean it

Romantic

To the people who have willingly given love
More than they have ever expected in
return
To the hopeless romantics
Who saw the red flags
Ignored them
And didn't learn

To the ones who want to forgive
But you can't forget what they did
In bed next to someone that you can't
stand
So you forget about being happy
Since y'all got kids

Love has no room for short cuts
Or nights where you can't get sleep
Saying sorry to a person you didn't do shit
to
Because if you don't
They'd be cool if y'all don't speak

Let someone fight for you
You've been putting in enough effort
For the both of y'all
Why waste your love on someone

Who can't do right by you

When you can use that love for you too
Because you deserve
Roses that never get old
A love that even on bad terms
You're still the one they'd call first

With good news
Someone you can vent to
Expressing how you feel
Isn't an argument in their eyes
But you shutting down is an issue

Because in love we communicate here
They run to God to find answers
To the problems you have
Instead of a stranger in a DM

That ain't you
Asking when can I see you
In their heart they know they'll never find
you
In the presence of someone else
Someone willing to give you
More than you ever felt

That chocolate in summer time love
Make me melt

Make the heartbreaks of my past make
sense
I'd go through it all again
If my story gets to end like this

Just because you can do it all on your own does not mean that you have to; you deserve a break, you deserve rest, you deserve someone who would never let you carry the weight of the world all by yourself.

MAUI THE WRITER

Beautiful Bliss

When was the last time you gave yourself a fair chance at being happy without questioning it? Without allowing the trauma from your past relationships to give you a million reasons why this time will be no different? You deserve to be happy, but when you are, you overthink it. It is hard for some of us to just live in and enjoy the moment because we have been let down so many times. We have mastered the art of not getting our hopes up or having too high of expectations for other people. Love has knocked on my door and I have looked through the peephole and pretended nobody was home. The girl on the other side of the door was sick of not being able to know the difference between a red flag and just someone who has potential. But if potential means having or showing the capacity to become something in the future, then I must admit I have labeled some men as having potential, even when they didn't show me shit. Other times I was too afraid and I ruined things before they even had a chance to grow into anything. I have swung my door wide open with a baseball bat screaming, "Who the hell is it this time?" Yet and still, we deserve to be happy. We deserve to understand what it is like to have clean slates and to let go of the baggage that we hold on so tightly to from everyone who has let us down.

We learn to create it on our own first and when our happiness is in abundance, we can invite someone in to enjoy what we created. As long as they promise to never take, or interrupt. If you open the door for love, I hope they add to or help maintain that happiness you created. I have lost my happiness so many times because of someone else. I no longer allow people to just come in here and start touching things.

Potentially

If you met your soulmate today would you be fine with who you are presenting to them? Are you comfortable with this version of yourself or would you be giving them someone who still has a lot of work and growing to do while hoping that they can see the potential in you? It is a gift to see the beauty in things that have not even reached their final form or fullest potential. It is a curse to allow your heart to play tricks on you and see potential where there isn't any just because it is what you feel like you should have at the moment. Your entitlement is why you hold on to things that are not even meant to be yours but you have convinced yourself are what you should have. It looks like what you want, it fits the dream that you have planned out for yourself and to you it isn't even about what it is in this moment but what it can become. We fall in love with potential and our daydreams that we create. We have to look at ourselves and the people around us with honesty. Who are we right now and who are the people around us? We get frustrated that people aren't who we want them to be or who we "thought" they were. Who were they when you met them? Who are they right now?

We get so disappointed when we invest so much of our time and love in someone who doesn't change into who we "potentially" thought they would for us. There we go, always thinking that our love can change someone or make them different; seeing potential in people who do not even see potential in themselves or have a desire to be anything more than who they are today. You have to be honest and stop lying to yourself all the damn time. Who the hell are you lying next to at night and who are you? Stop making excuses for things that are in a person's character so that you do not feel so ashamed that you continue to stay, saying things like, "They are a liar but they are a good person deep inside," "They want to change, they just don't know how to," then, before you know it, years have gone by and you are still making excuses for someone hoping that they "potentially" turn into the person who will fit perfectly into your dream that you created for yourself.

We cannot change anyone; we can only change ourselves or change how we deal with these people.

Ms. Independent

This page is dedicated to those who have been doing everything on their own for so long that they've forgotten how to allow someone to do something for them. Your "I don't need anyone" energy has pushed people away who have taken your word for it. I want your ass to learn how to relax and allow someone to be there for you. Just because you can do so much on your own and you got this doesn't mean you have to do it all alone. You deserve to receive the love that you give to everyone else for once, without the fear of being let down and feeling uncomfortable being catered to. You have been showing up for yourself for so long that you don't even know how to ask for help even when you really need it, you are so accustomed to figuring everything out all on your own.

A person who loves you will not only want to show up for you, but other people need to feel needed too. How can I show you how much I am willing to do for you if you never allow me to be there for you? Your independence is beautiful but so is partnership. You having a partner that shows up for you does not overshadow the fact that you are independent and can do things on your own. Your partner is there to remind you that even though you can do so much so gracefully, you do not always have to.

Now, a person who is comfortable with watching you do so much for everyone around you, including them, and they never so much as ask if you need help is a real issue. I will never be able to wrap my head around someone who claims to love you watching you struggle. Do not be afraid to allow someone to show up for you, and do not be afraid to let go of the people who never do.

Independent

Free from outside control; not depending on another's authority.

Six

Monica

I do not even feel like going in this house right now because I know my man is going to be upset with me. I walk in the house and I waste no time in getting right to the point so that I can just get this out of the way. "Hey my Devon baby, I missed you all day, best boyfriend in the world."

Extremely unimpressed by my antics, he replies, "Monica, what did your ass do now because you are just way too happy to see me?"

"Well, baby, I went to get some new tires, I got my oil changed and a car wash after work."

"Monica, why would you go do all of that after I said that I would do it for you in the morning? You are always so busy trying to prove how independent you are that you can't even let me be a man. I love that you are self-sufficient, but what do you need me for besides dick, if I can't even be there for you?"

I feel bad and do not have much to say except, "I know … it's just I already had to drive past it."

I take off of my jacket, wash my hands and go to the kitchen to get everything out to get dinner started. Devon loves my Alfredo so that's exactly what I am going to make for him tonight so he can relax. I yell, "Baby, do you want some Alfredo?"

"No, I am going to my mom's to eat, you can have dinner alone since you love being the man in this relationship." He walks out of the front door before I even have a chance to say something back to his smart-ass comment.

I love Devon and I am sure any girl would love to be with someone who not only is a great guy but strives to be a great provider for his woman. The only thing that he complains about is that I am too independent. I used to think that a man saying things like, "A woman is too independent," was their way of being upset she won't be controlled by them. But Devon was just raised in a household where his dad did everything for his mom; even though his mom was successful, his dad made sure small things were never something she had to do herself. I am not his mom though, I do not need a man and I definitely do not need a man ever thinking that I have to depend on him for anything. I have been handling my business before a man; I will handle it while having one and even after.

He also says that I don't know how to talk to people; "It is not what you say, it is how you say it" is what he always tells me. People be having me fucked up though. Let me also add that I am a Leo and he is a Leo too. We are both really strong-minded, but I do not want to lose my man or my independence. I have been looking out for myself for a long time and one relationship that I was in, he would throw everything he did for me in my face. I had become so dependent on him financially and emotionally. I made a promise to myself that I would never let someone have that much power or control over me. I know Devon doesn't want to control me, he wants us to be partners and for me to know that I can always count on him. I know that if I want this to work I have to trust him to lead and I can probably change how I talk to people. I am getting too old to still say things like, "That's just how I talk" especially if my delivery hurts the feelings of my friends and people I care about. I would hate to lose people I love because of my inability to take a look at myself. I am an independent woman who has been doing things for herself for a long time and I damn sure aint going to stop now. But if a person wants to come into my life, not to take my independence away but to make it easier, maybe I should let them. There is nothing wrong with allowing someone to show up for you, especially when you have shown up for everyone else for so long.

Fair Chance

It's been a while
Since you gave yourself a fair chance
At being happy
At feeling magic

Bragging about being independent
You can't allow anyone to take control
Give you what you deserve
Or do things without you asking

You love so hard that you don't even trust
yourself
You don't trust the person you become
In bed next to someone you would do
anything for
Because what if they wouldn't do the same
for you

While the person who made you this way
Is somewhere still doing what makes
themselves happy
I think it's time that you get on the same
shit too
And stop being afraid

Or thinking of all the things that could go
wrong
Finding reasons why you don't like
someone
In the middle of a first date

Ruining things before they start
By comparing them to your past
relationships
Because you wasted years with someone
You should have never been with

Or planned your life with someone
Who turned out not to be shit
You deserve bliss

You deserve
Something softer than rose petals
I thinks it's time you let love catch you

Toxic Sex

I used to think the best sex was with my toxic ex that I couldn't leave alone. That the best dick came from the person that you have been with for forever but break up all the time and always get back together because the sex is so good. Some of us actually pride ourselves in the fact that we've never had sex with anyone else. Even with knowing this person is a liar, having sex with other women and will never give us more than some half ass love we still feel good knowing that we will never share our body with anyone else. The satisfaction that we find in allowing someone to sexually have access to us whenever they please and still treat us like shit while we sit around waiting for the next time that we see them or get to spend time with them is not where our happy endings will happen. We lower our worth every time we wake up out of our sleep at 3am to reply to a text message and pack a spend the night bag. Every time we try to shower, shave, get dressed, fix our hair and pack all before they get there so we can be at the door on time, we disrespect ourselves. Why are you giving someone access to your body that doesn't want access to any other part of you? If we really think the reason he cannot leave us alone is because our sex is so good, maybe we should consider that maybe it is also because we are the only ones who continuously allows them to save us for when it is convenient to them. The best sex is with someone who loves and values you. The best sex is with the person who takes their time to make sure they give you other forms of intimacy other than just physical. It is the person who you can kiss and don't have to wonder were they kissing the person they cheated on you with the same way.

Tested

It's easy to say forever
When your relationship ain't been tested
Or your love hasn't faced any challenges

When not hurting your best-friend is more
important
Than proving your point over some stupid
shit
When your pride doesn't exist
So you can communicate during an
argument

In a place where true love has no room for
ego
And we use time apart for self reflection
Instead of fucking other people

Where the only home that my lips know
Are against yours
In a fantasy full of nasty things
Where once is never enough and I need
more

Where if what's mine is really yours and
vise versa
We don't count favors or keep score

It's my pleasure to bring you peace in this
world
You've provided me with heaven in yours

You lay next to me
And I stare at you while you sleep
A blessing in the flesh
I have a prayer underneath my sheets

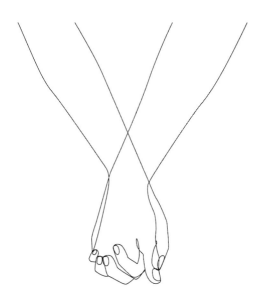

Being nasty won't make him change,
keep your vagina to yourself.

MAUI THE WRITER

FOOD COURT LOVE

You ever think about why when you walk through the food court in the mall you take the sesame chicken sample from the Chinese restaurant even though your butt never gets food from there, even though the chicken sample is actually pretty good? We have a tendency to entertain things that are continuously offered and available to us just because they're there. Why does he keep coming over to your house even though he say,"he doesn't want a relationship and doesn't want to be with you? Because there is a good woman, sex, a listening ear, friend and food there. Someone who has made themselves readily available to them whenever they are in the mood for it, with no plans of taking what you offer seriously… Still they indulge because you offer. Stop allowing how much you like a person to have you out here being treated like a food court sample, overextending yourself to someone to prove how much of a good woman you are. Or you're craving their company so much that you have decided to settle and accept them at any capacity they will allow you to have them. So you settle for quality time with no commitment, no date nights, no surprise flowers, just bare-minimum treatment and sex. If you are the catch, then carry yourself like one; luxury doesn't have to convince. Rolls Royce isn't out here with commercials saying, "Try me." A person who is truly interested in you will not have to be convinced or negotiated with.

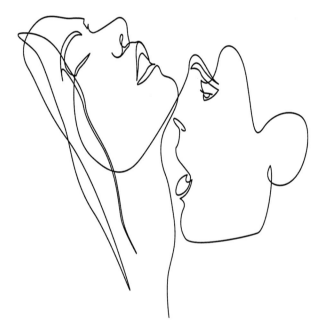

Pussy Talk

There is too much casual sex and not enough sex with someone we have a connection with or care for. We are so used to instant gratification that we are just out here rushing everything, even if it involves our body. I don't even understand the logic behind some of us liking a guy so much that we think if we really put the pussy on him he will act right or treat us good. I like my good man up front and in cash before I ever sprinkle a little WAP on him.

When you have been talking to a guy and you find out he's a clown, you're not upset that you were a part of the circus; you're upset that you had sex with a clown! You moved too fast and put your best moves on somebody's undeserving-ass son. Now the question is was it because you didn't take your time or because you have needs and he texted you on a vulnerable night when you just so happened to be horny and lonely? You're so disgusted by him now that you don't even want to tell your girlfriends what you did. This is all because we act on emotions and impulse instead of patience and logic.

I want you to take your time and give the most intimate parts of yourself to someone you have a real connection with or care for. Because one thing I have learned is if you ordered a good man and received a clown, you can't get a refund or your pussy back when the item isn't as described.

The love for yourself has to be stronger than your desire to be loved by someone else. Make sure you show up for you first.

MAUI THE WRITER

Seven

Sade

I know Ryan wishes things between us could go back to how they were when we first met, but thats not who I am now. When he met me I was a woman who wasn't completely sure of what she wanted and someone who would do anything to be in his company. I was so attracted to him that I agreed to things that I no longer agree with now. When we met he told me that he didn't want a relationship and I told him I felt the same way, out of fear he would distance himself from me. He just wanted someone who he could spend the night with occasionally. So we became friends with benefits. But now that it has been months of us having some of the best sex that I have had in my life my feelings are completely different.

We have sex, he spends the night, all my friends know him, yet he still keeps telling me that titles don't mean anything. He confuses me because he does not want a relationship but would be mad if I went out with someone else or brought up the idea of me getting into a relationship. I hate that my feelings for him have gotten so strong that it would be hard for me to stop seeing him when I am in so deep emotionally. I know that I am the type of girl who loves being in a relationship, so I am mad at myself that I agreed to some shit that I knew would never satisfy me. I knew that a relationship that was nothing more than sex would never be able to please me but I did not want to risk not having him in my life. I still don't understand why wouldn't a man want to be with someone who is already showing them that they can please them? I wish I never started having sex with his ass or I at least had a receipt to get my vagina and the meals I cooked for him back. I could have saved all of what I have been giving him for someone who actually would appreciate it. Now here I am trying to convince him that we should be together and it makes more sense for him to be in a committed relationship with the woman who is giving him everything that he wants already with no titles.

Just Once

What if we only get to experience
A love like this once
And everything else I felt
I had it mistaken it for
What was just lust or fun

I'm afraid we'll grow apart
Or this won't end in a fairytale
I'll tell my grandkids about the time
I looked love in the eyes and almost fell

But the timing was off
And if my sanctuary is being wrapped in
your arms
My peace is somewhere still lingering on
the hoodie
With your cologne you let me keep

Tears dripping over photos of you and me
Why do I somehow feel like the fool is me
So willing to risk it all for you
Tell me would you do the same for me

Because overthinking steals your joy
But investing my time is someone
Who can never fully love me back

Will hurt me more

If you asked me
I'd be yours
But
The timing is so off
I'm glad that our paths crossed
I'm thankful for love lost

Allow love to be there for you instead of being afraid that things will turn out how they always do. Stop ruining things before they begin all because you want to protect yourself.

Communication

The relationships I have been in where anything I said turned into an argument have made me realize a person's level of understanding is just as important as my delivery. I kept trying to talk to people who did not know how to communicate or articulate their emotions properly. All they knew how to do was get defensive, get mad and turn the whole conversation into an argument. There have also been times when I did not know how to communicate how I felt in a mature way so I would resort to just getting upset and hoping that my partner could see something was bothering me. Nobody wants to play charades just as much as we do not want to play; let me be careful what I say. What you say does not matter if you are talking to someone who is not even willing to listen or who only listens to respond but not to actually understand. How can you fully love someone who does not even allow you the space to express the way you feel? Who shuts you out or makes you regret even trying to talk to them? Now here you are lying in bed, crying next to a person who won't ask you, "What's wrong?" because they never want to communicate or be accountable. What is so hurtful is how much you love them but you cannot force them to learn how to communicate. It is hard to build a solid foundation when you are missing one of the key ingredients.

How many times are you going to have the same conversation with someone about how they do not know how to communicate before you feel like you are wasting your breath? If they do not know how to talk to you, maybe it is time they started talking to themselves. Especially if no effort or at least the will to try is being shown.

Pride

Our desires to have our partners communicate with us properly have to come with the same accountability in the midst of our silent treatments and attitudes. During a car ride, gazing out the window knowing exactly what we are upset about but instead just saying, "I'm not mad," when we are asked is not fair when we are trying to build a foundation with proper communication. Yet we still go home slamming cabinets, huffing and puffing, just waiting for our partner's mind-reading capabilities to kick in. Is it fair for someone to try to play this guessing game with a grown-ass adult? Hours of trying to figure out why someone is mad when they simply can just communicate. We should be communicating without fear and not feeling like if we express how we feel our voices will not be heard. We will never know if we do not try.

Honesty

The quality of being honest

Eight

Jason

She left me when I needed her the most. I know it would have been selfish for me to ask her to stay, while I fought my own battles emotionally. But sometimes I think of how different things would be if I had communicated that I was depressed. I loved her through everything she went through and when it was her turn to show up for me, she didn't. I expected her to just "know". I would sleep so much and she'd wake me up asking, "What chick you fucked, that got you so sleepy?" I just didn't have anything worth waking up for.

It was never another woman and I hate that I allowed her to create her own assumptions instead of being honest. I watched her try to do so many different

156

things to make me happy, but I was in a dark place that I had to get out of on my own. I learned so much about myself and about the extents a woman would go, to please a man. She would have done anything to get me to go back to who she knew. I know it is not easy loving someone through their dark days but if they don't know how you feel, how can they be there for you? I never gave her a chance to show me if she would be there for me. I just pushed her away and made myself hard to love. I figured that would be easier than feeling like someone skipped out on me when I needed them. I had too much pride and didn't want to admit how much I needed someone. Love has no room for pride and ego. I see now that a person who loves you will love you even on the days you don't love yourself or think you are worth loving. But that can't happen if you force their hand to take their love away.

Love has no room for egos too big to communicate and pride too strong to apologize.

No Room

Love has no room for your attitude
You're only mad at me because I was mad
at you
Leave your bullshit at the door and your
ego too
Cuz I love you so much I might apologize
for shit
I know I ain't do

Your pride is too big to admit when you're
wrong
So if we don't talk you're cool
And I hate the fact
I can't go a day without
Hearing from you

But you see no reason to value you
What you aren't afraid to lose
Cuz my ass comes right back
After saying I'm done with you

I just want you to fight for me
The way I would for you
I deserve more than a three word text
After pouring my heart out to you

I deserve more than you getting your shit
together
Once you see me happy
Once I lost 10 pounds or
I got that toxic shit from around me

Then all it takes is one text from you
For me to feel like I'm drowning
Cuz you know I'd cut everyone off
If it meant me and you could finally be
happy

But
Not this time
Not again
This is where our story ends

It does not matter how much it might hurt, I will heal. I will be gentle with myself and not rush.
But I will never go back to some shit that I know never loved me back.

Impressive

Do you ever wonder how you get out of one really bad relationship just for your ass to end up in another one or end up in a complicated situationship, thinking to yourself, *What the hell am I doing?* When we do not fully heal from the last place that we were in or at least learn a lesson, we repeat the same mistakes. Other times we are so busy trying to heal our wounds with a new person that we do not realize that they aren't a Band-Aid, only a distraction from how we really feel. Sex with a new person or texting five people cannot make you forget about the pain you might have felt or the person you still care for. If we do not have our shit figured out, we will find ourselves in emotionally vulnerable places being impressed by the first nice person we meet. Love is meant to feel like home, but if you are coming from a love that has made you feel abandoned, you will just be grateful to have anywhere to lay your head.

We get so amazed and wrapped up in things that feel so fulfilling when we haven't felt those emotions in so long. We move so quickly that we do not even see the red flags we skipped right on by with this new person. Do not be one of those people who are at a place in their lives where they are not sure if they really like a person or if they are just bored. The love for yourself is the first home you have to learn to love, appreciate and maintain. If we invest in the love we have for ourselves, the only thing we will be impressed with is a love that feels similar or greater than what we have learned to give to us.

It doesn't matter how good it feels in the moment, if you know it will never be able to measure up to what you need. Stop settling for temporary satisfaction and learn to be patient for what you deserve.

MAUI THE WRITER

Ole Self-Loving Ass

This beautiful self-love journey that everyone tries to make you believe is full of self-care Sundays, facials with your girlfriends and too many mimosas during brunch is far from it. This journey gets lonely at night; it is looking in the mirror some days asking yourself, "Is there something wrong with me?" It is crying yourself to sleep and wondering why you feel so guilty for letting go of people who only hurt you. There are going to be days when you just want some sex more than you want to wait for a soulmate or some healing you aren't even sure is going to happen. But somewhere in the middle of the dinner date alone, that you took yourself on, the five pounds you just lost and the plant that you bought last week that you gave a name to you'll find happiness. You won't be looking for someone to come along to fill a void you have or to kiss the wounds of some trauma that needs addressing. You will have found your own accountability, your newfound love for yourself and happiness that you have learned to create on your own. Those long nights you thought you would never get through are now what you have learned to enjoy and appreciate. Too busy loving on yourself to accept some shit less than what you have learned to give to you, and now your standards are different. You're glowing from within and every day you are working on yourself. The best part about this journey is it did not have shit to do with anyone else. It was all for you, and it has been about you all along.

Rebirth

The action of reappearing or starting to flourish or increase after a decline; revival.

Nine

Kim

I bought myself flowers today. A dozen of Daffodils, since they symbolize new beginnings and fresh starts. I feel better than I did last week when I was feeling as if, the person I loved so much ripped my heart out of my chest. Last week I felt empty, like I lost my best friend and the love of my life in one day. I think this is the hardest breakup that I have ever experienced but I am being gentle with myself.

I have been trying not to let my friends tell me how to feel or to not cry over his ain't shit ass, while still allowing them to support me. I am feeling every emotion that I need to feel and not running from any of it. I want to heal not hide. I gave all of the love I had to that relationship even on the days I did not even have any love for myself. Even when he heard me crying on the phone asking him, "Why do this to me, someone who has been with you through everything?" He did not even have anything to say, just silent. I wasn't even worth an explanation or an apology. Maybe a part of me just wanted to hear him lie to me one last time and say there isn't another woman like I think it is and he just needs some space to get himself together. That would have kept me hopeful but thats not what I needed, I needed it to hurt the way it did.

I needed him to make me feel the pain that I feel now so I can finally move on, if he didn't I would have spent my life being naive. Last week I was feeling like there was no reason for me to live, I felt like I no longer had a purpose. How did I let someone make me feel like there is no reason to live without them? My value and purpose is so much greater than who I am loved by, I am so much more. So here I am with a dozen of Daffodils, with so many reasons to live even without a relationship.

Glowing

You look so much better when you're
happy
When you're glowing
When you finally start putting yourself first
And learned the definition of what no is

The definition of fuck this shit
The beauty in allowing yourself to rest and
recharge
And patting yourself on the back even if a
Whole lot of nothing is all you did

You're so strong
Even when you don't want to be
Or you're tired

Even when you told them last time
Don't ask you for shit no more
It's in your heart to still give
To show up for others
To always come through

I hope in the mist of you sharing your love
You save some for you too
Save some for yourself
Because you'll need it

You'll have so much of it
That you'll be cool with whoever's not
meant for you leaving

You won't even follow
You know you'll be fine
You be so tired
But you always try

You don't even ask for help
Even when you really want to
You're so used to doing things for you
I hope you know people who love you
Won't mind
And they will show up for you

I'm still wondering how you do it all
So if nobody told you in a while
I see you, I admire you, you motivate me
and I'm proud of you

Are You That Somebody?

Do you remember who you were before you gave too much love to the wrong people? I have given a lot to people who made me feel like I had to water down how I love. Pieces of what made me who I am were missing by the time these relationships ended. I always said, "I wasn't affectionate," but I actually really am. I just was forcing love on people who would say I was clingy, to give them space or they just were not in the mood. This has made some of us feel like we are always doing too much, so we just do less of who we naturally are. We have molded ourselves into what makes us easier to love.
Then some others have taken what they have so much of to give and locked it away. We lock away different parts of ourselves that we think are the hardest to love and

then someone comes along making you feel so comfortable that you unbox what you have kept hidden. Certain people just bring out certain sides of us that no one has been able to before. Other times we find a way to pour those things into ourselves instead of looking to give someone parts of us we are not sure they will appreciate. Who were you before you loved so many of the wrong people? Stop hiding parts of yourself because you are uncomfortable giving yourself to someone who you know doesn't deserve you in the first place. Go where you can unbox everything that you have kept hidden and it is welcomed with open arms. All of the love that you have to give, all of the romantic things you like to do, the stories you tell, or even the time alone with yourself that you still value. Who knows, maybe all of this time you actually have been really affectionate and your soul hasn't come across someone worth bringing that side out for.

90's R&B Love

I wish you a 90s R&B type of love
Or a romantic comedy
Like one of those low budget movies on
Netflix
That didn't seem interesting at first
But ended up having a good message

A love that doesn't require you
To beg for how you want to be treated
I got you something when I was at the mall
You crossed my mind
I thought you would need this

I bought a life jacket for you my love
For the days when this world becomes too
Much
And you think you're sinking

Though I can't carry no burdens for you
I promise you'll never have to face them
Alone
And you know they mean it

A love that knows what you thinking
They can hear you even when you aren't
speaking

Love that thinks of you first
A love that isn't selfish and possessive
That prefers you putting yourself first

Never desiring you to love them
More than you love you
Someone that doesn't make you feel like
They don't have time
You aren't worth it
Or they have to make space for you

Somewhere in this crowd I found you
We found love
And even though it's in a wrapping I least
expected
It's exactly what I want
How did you know

How do I take care of something
I never experienced
But always wanted
And expect it to grow
I want to grow old with you
Whoever you are

I am waiting for our
90's R&B type of love

Effort

Something I have learned, which is so simple yet important, is effort is a reflection of interest. What would a person who is truly interested in you gain by leaving you room to question where you stand in their life? A person who is interested in you will put forth the effort to show you. It is also your job to take your time to get to know people even if they are showing effort because my next question is what are their intentions? And do their intentions with you align with what you are looking for at this point in your life? We have all witnessed people who put forth effort just for sex, just to have you fall in love and completely change, or the people who put forth effort but have no desire to commit to anything serious. The only disappointment we should have after continuing to put forth effort where it isn't reciprocated is with ourselves. Why are we entertaining people who do not show us any signs of being interested in us outside of just the physical? So ask yourself, "How does being around this person make me feel? Do I feel like I am overextending myself to them and showing more interest than they are? A person can put forth effort just to waste your time so it is also your job to make sure you aren't allowing anyone to not only waste your time but not value your presence either. What is genuine will not need to be questioned; it will not need to be forced, it will just flow.

Fate

The development of events beyond a person's control, regarded as determined by a supernatural power

Ten

Candice

He had met me at a place in my life where thirsty Thursdays and dinner alone at my favorite restaurant were more important than me falling in love. I had done the inner work, I had learned to enjoy my own company and love myself. I just no longer cared about putting a time line on my life for when things needed to happen for me. I see people come into my therapy office all the time who thought they would be married with kids at their age or living out their dreams. They come in obsessing over their life not going according to their perfect plan or their vision boards they made in high school. I tell them that faith and fear cannot coexist. Either you trust the timing of everything in your life or spend forever not appreciating the things that you have, because you are too worried you won't wake up one day to even more. I refuse to let that be me. I want to flow with the progress of my life, because I know I will ruin things if I rush them.

It was 6:45am and I was hitting the snooze button on my phone as usual. I go to yoga every morning with my girlfriends, Brandy, Rasheeda and Danielle. I finally mustered up some energy to jump in the shower, brush my teeth, get dressed and leave. Even with me being tired I still get there early. I come in and see them in the back of the yoga studio and they're gossiping as usual. Rasheeda is talking about the guy she was with last night, with her outrageous ass stories. All Brandy and Danielle do is just listen to her and laugh. She has a story for any scenario you can think of. We still have five more minutes left for the yoga instructor and the guest instructor come.

There is a guest instructor every week, I guess to bring more people in or for the class to not get bored with the same routines every week; either way I am here every week to spend time with my girls. I work so much that this yoga class or going out with them whenever our schedules align are the highlights of most of my weeks.

The instructor walks in and there he was. This man, who was about 6'4 and had the softest looking brown skin I had ever seen. He didn't even look like the guest instructors that normally come in, he looked more like he played sports or could be a professor. "Okay we getting sexy instructors now" Brandy says while she's drinking her water trying not to laugh.

The instructor greets us and says, "Hey everyone this is our guest instructor for the day Drew, he's a sports therapist". He is used to helping all types of athlete's with stretching and has been doing it for years, let us show him how we stretch here in our yoga class. Everyone pair up with their partner, Candice you can pair up with the guest since both of you will be speaking at my event next month, I want you to get to know each other. I look at Danielle to see if she can read my mind and she just looks at me and starts laughing. I am always so awkward around guys. She says, "Don't be scared now, let his sexy ass stretch you out".

He comes over towards me and I reach my hand out to shake his and say, "Hey I'm Candice".

He responds "That's a nice name, I'm Drew..So what kind of therapist are you Candice"?

Then it all began. From that one conversation in yoga class. We exchanged numbers that day and never went a day without talking to each other. Even when he went out of town for two weeks for work he would come back to his hotel room, put his phone on speaker, lay down and I would tell him all about my day. When he finally got back in town, our first date was out to brunch at this place not far from my office. I remember just sitting across the table from him feeling like this is him. This has to be who I'm meant to be with.

There were other guys I had been talking to but there were no time for them with how much consistency and effort he put in to spend time with me. The interest he showed in me was nothing compared to the men I had been talking to for months and it still had not gone anywhere. So I did what felt right. I allowed him to just show me how it feels being around someone, who not only makes how they feel clear but reciprocates what I give.

Even on the days I would overthink and try to push him away out of fear, he would tell me, "One day at time". He would always say things like, if a person is treating you well and making you happy, don't ruin it by focusing on what could go wrong.

I was afraid of how I felt. I had never been in love that was easy and understanding. All the love that I knew, came with a two month honey moon phase and someone who would end up being a liar, cheater or a person just not compatible with me.

We talked about everything when we were together, our families, past relationships, our careers. Anything we could think of we would talk about and never with any judgement. It is a relief being in the presence of someone who you don't have to water down or hide parts of yourself with. Where you know someone won't throw any of what you say in your face but use it to love you better.

Every Wednesday it was something new he would surprise me with. We met on a Wednesday, so he considered every Wednesday our anniversary. He made sure that we always dated. From something as simple to a walk at night, flowers or dinner, he would make sure I felt special. I knew he loved me and I loved him too but was too afraid to say it first.

Love had no room for my fears, or my reasons for being too afraid to just fall. I have fell in the past, right into the direction of someone who didn't catch me. Your future doesn't have any room for the things from your past that hold you back. The day he said he loved me, I did not even respond immediately. I replied, "What did you just say?" Just to make sure I was hearing what I thought I heard correctly. His actions showed me he loved me before he ever got a chance to say it. I was smiling so hard and didn't have anything else to say besides, I love you too. I get to be in love and still be an individual. I still go to yoga classes and dinner with my friends. I still make time for me. The fact that I am still showing up for myself makes love easier. I am not looking for any voids to be filled and everything from him is extra on top of what I have learned to always give to myself. He met me when thirsty Thursday's and dinner alone were what I looked forward to. Now my dinners are not so lonely, my Thursdays are for therapy and wine down Wednesdays are all for me. I know now that a healthy love will only change you for the better, sometimes it shows up when you least expect it. Even though everyday won't be a perfect love, it's making a conscious decision that as long as there is effort, everyday I will choose you and choose to love you even through bad days.

Simple

My legs across your lap
I'm rubbing your beard
I thought affection wasn't really what I was
into

But I guess when you force love on people
Who don't deserve it for so long
There would be parts of yourself that you'd
forget too

Firm in what you believe in
You have a soft spot for me
You're gentle

You leave
Yo ass need to hurry up
I miss you

Are we codependent
Or is for once reality better than a dream
This the only fantasy we want to live in

I said I would never cook for a man
With some bare minimum ass love
You give me everything in abundance
Meet me in the kitchen
I'll be dessert after I make your dinner

I was used to my opinion ending in
arguments
Am I talking to much
No finish
You always listen

Clean slates trying not
To project past traumas
On a story that is still being written
As if I already know the ending

A broken heart
And an empty night stand
With tissue
Lets replace that with a family picture
We can turn our lives into something
We weren't really sure existed

No Mistakes

It's no mistakes when it comes to fate
Or alignment
Just lessons that we learn after mistakes
That all lead us to perfect timing

Let my heart be the home you find rest in
Your two for one special
Where you found
Your soulmate and your best-friend

Don't overthink
Just fall
Love will catch you
Even your flaws are beautiful
In the eyes of someone
Who thinks your special

No fear
Just flowing
In the bed with someone
You don't have to question
Got you glowing

Your love turns my body into your ocean
Where everything is reciprocated
There is no hesitation with being open

Don't overthink
Just fall
If they knew where they were meant to be
They wouldn't be upset about what didn't work
Or a love that didn't last
Or people that refused to put them first
Everything about love I enjoy the most
I learned from being hurt

No fear
Just flowing
Your body next to mine
Somebody got you glowing

Healing

How can we know how much healing we need to do if we keep hiding or running from what we fear the most? How much have you grown or healed when you're sitting across from what used to trigger you? We can't avoid things and convince ourselves we are healed. We have to be able to be in the same room with our demons and know that the peace of mind we have found isn't worth losing by acting based off of impulse or insecurities. There are a lot of things that didn't deserve a reaction from you, but in the mist of emotions and irrational thinking make sure your ass does not throw away all of the inner work that you have done for yourself. When shit around you isn't adding up, just be still and breathe. Things always unfold on their own; we don't even have to get out of character.

Risk

I dare you
To risk it all for love
Even though you're afraid

Because the last time
You gave your heart away
They paid you in minimum wage
You got the short end of the stick

You speak up
Then they guilt trip
Even though you've put up
With so much of their shit

And even though y'all got years in and
children
Or the memories in the beginning
Make you believe deep down inside
That is still them

Make sure you don't destroy yourself
While trying to heal them
Paranoid that love can't do anything more
than hurt
And it has been your gift and your curse
trying to force things to work

Being everyone's savior

Now you attract takers
The ungrateful
Or people so convinced you'll never leave
That they save you for later

I ain't got time for that shit
My love ain't always unconditional
Sometimes the condition is
That they are willing to reciprocate
What I'm ready to give

And their eager to take
I can't always pour
And I know they can't always replace

Sometimes its okay to take everything
Just to go start over new
Or take the love you have given to
Everyone else
And start giving that love to you

Eleven

Chloe

Unlearning was so much more than letting go of the way that I think, there was a certain level of healing that had to happen so that I could let go of everything that was holding me back. There was the built up resentment from childhood and the feeling of my parents letting me down. Then the relationships I continued to find myself in with people that did not care about me at all or at least in the way that I needed someone to care for me. There was the looking for my partners to fill voids, then the trust issues and fear of abandonment. Learning to let go of the things that I was holding onto so that I could view life differently.

I had been in relationships for so long pointing the finger at men for the things that they had done to me, for them taking my kindness for granted or hurting me. When I started being accountable for the role that I played by not only choosing these partners but staying with them after I knew exactly who they were, I looked at love differently. Things were so much different when I could look at myself and identify exactly what I needed to do differently also. Some people will never reach a level of understanding within themselves because they don't want to be honest. Can you imagine spending your life telling lies to yourself? I was afraid to be alone so I accepted my partners for whatever portion of themselves they decided to give me. I would apologize first because in my heart I felt as if nobody would ever love me enough to fight for me or say sorry to me for what they had done. My life was full of settling for less than I deserved because I did not know exactly what it was that I deserved. I did not know about what triggered me, I didn't know about childhood trauma or even what made me happy.

I had to learn all of those things by first letting go of what I thought that I knew. I had to work on myself and do it without the expectation of anyone being proud of me or even noticing. My desire to be accepted and acknowledged by my parents would have me doing so many things for validation or to be a constant people pleaser. But nobody can see the inner work you are doing for yourself and thats the most beautiful part of it. You are doing all the work for you. The people around you in your future will reap the benefits of the work that you put in for yourself.

I would tell myself that when I have children they won't have to heal themselves from a childhood where they felt unloved like I did or look for their sense of importance in the relationships that they are in. Even if I get married one day I will be coming into the life of my husband as a woman that is whole and not a woman who doesn't know who she is, what makes her happy or cannot communicate. He will be meeting someone who speaks affirmations of love, peace and goodness over her life. Someone who is kind but has boundaries and will let you know she doesn't play that shit. Who doesn't hide parts of herself or try to make herself easier to love for people who are not meant for her. Someone who listens not to respond but to understand and learn. More importantly the things that I have learned about myself will help me to choose a more healthier love and also love others in a healthier way.

All of the pouring into ourselves that we do and all of the unlearning, is an investment into us showing up as the highest versions of ourselves.

It is okay to wake up one day and decide that you no longer want to settle for the things that you have for in the past. It is okay to wake up and decide that you will no longer settle for less. No matter what you have settled for in the past, you are allowed to increase the price on your worth.

MAUI THE WRITER

Unlearning

A part of healing is unlearning. It is getting out of your own way and letting go of the unhealthy parts of you so that you can grow. It is making space for growth and for things that are in alignment with where you are going. Be gentle with yourself on this journey, there are so many things that you have been doing for years and habits that you have had forever. As you shed this old layer of who you have outgrown, understand that it is okay to make mistakes. You are the teacher and the student. Give yourself some good advice, positive affirmations and stick to the boundaries that you are creating. Don't feel bad for creating boundaries when the people who have benefited from taking advantage of you make you feel guilty about choosing yourself. You have all the tools that you need to be able to attract what you are deserving of, it is completely up to you if you want to settle for some shit or master the art of patience. Just know that if you do decide to settle that it is all by choice and habit. What is important is what we learn and how we react now that we are unlearning.

The End

Acknowledgment prayer

MAUI THE WRITER

God,

Whatever it is that you have for me, prepare me for it. Make me ready, make me whole and help me come to a place where I can accept good things and not find reasons to self-sabotage them. I have been specific before in the past and I realize that I don't always know what I need or want and I always end up feeling like I am missing something. So help me become full on my own so I don't search for what's missing inside of me in others. I have been through some situations that still hurt me a lot; I have been let down and disappointed, so help me to trust. I have also been the one who has hurt people by projecting pain on them that I kept bottled inside, so help me find peace so that I don't hurt others because I am hurting. Allow me to enter new beginnings with an open but rational mind and a clean slate. I don't want to bring my baggage to new places anymore. I don't want my past to have me afraid of everything because I'm so worried about being hurt. I want to be comfortable with my own company so I will be okay with letting things go that aren't for me and I don't feel the need to force or beg them to stay. Help me be able to see the difference between what I want for myself and what you want for me so that my desires and impatience do not continue to be why I settle. I don't want anything if you ain't the one who sent it, period.